Rookie Fire Truck

Illustrated by Jim Talbot

Written by Colin Alkars

ISBN: 0-7853-1667-1

Rookie is a brand new fire truck. He's excited about his first day at the firehouse.

Big Red is the oldest fire truck at the station. He laughs because Rookie has never fought a fire.

The other trucks are not nice to Rookie, either. They're jealous that he is so shiny and new, so Rookie decides to stay outside.

One night the alarm sounds. Rookie zooms into action and is the first to leave the station.

Rookie is about to spray the fire when Big Red shows up. "Outta my way, Rookie. I'll handle this," says Big Red.

The older trucks take over, and there is no room for Rookie to help. As he watches, Rookie sees something terrible.

Big Red has run out of water and is surrounded by flames! Rookie goes over to help at once.

Rookie puts out the fire and saves Big Red. The fire trucks are all sorry for being mean to Rookie, especially Big Red.